Frogspawn in the Pond

'aw' and 'au'

saw

paw

claws

yawned

crawl

crawled

frogspawn

caught

Bean was sitting by the pond. He could see two frogs in the water. Bean yawned and he went to sleep.

When he woke up, the frogs had gone. Bean saw

some blobs of jelly, all stuck together, floating in

the pond.

There were little black dots in the middle of the jelly. It was frogspawn. The black dots were tiny tadpoles.

Then Bean saw a toad crawl from under a
stone. It slid into the pond and it swam down
to the bottom.

Suddenly, the toad came up next to the

frogspawn. It opened its mouth very wide and

took a mouthful of it.

Bean jumped into the water. He grabbed the

toad with his paws. His claws dug into the toad.

It did not move.

Bean put the toad back on the grass. It
crawled away and hid under the stone. It did
not go into the pond again.

Then Bean caught a fish trying to eat the
frogspawn. He caught a bird trying to peck it
too.

The tiny tadpoles grew longer. They moved about in the jelly. Soon they were free and they could swim in the pond.

The tadpoles grew legs. Their tails shrank. They became little frogs. They hopped out of the pond to grow into big frogs on the land.

Vowels:

ai/ay/a-e:	again tails away became came
ee/ea:	sleep free see Bean eat
i-e/y/i:	wide trying by tiny
o/o-e:	opened go woke tadpoles stone
ow/oa:	grow toad floating
oo/ew:	too soon grew
oo:	took
ow/ou:	down mouth mouthful about out
er:	water together under longer
ir:	bird
aw/au:	paw saw claws frogspawn crawl crawled yawned caught
-y:	jelly tiny suddenly very

Verbs:

-ed verbs:	yawned opened grabbed crawled moved hopped jumped
Others:	was went had were slid swam came caught saw dug did put hid grew became took shrank

Exceptions: two water gone some there their move they could